Author: Bo Gramfors
The author writes books. It can be a fiction book, which is like a story, or a non fiction book like this one, which tells facts.

Editor: Siv Eklund
This editor assisted the author in the production of the book. She checked to make sure all the facts are correct.

Production: Lovell Johns, Oxford
This company made all the maps and put together all the text that the author wrote. They also made the film from which the book was printed.

Illustrators: Kevin Baverstock and Hardlines, Oxford.
Per Nævik, Stockholm
These are the artists, called illustrators, who drew all the pictures in the book.

Book Design: Kjeld Brandt, Copenhagen
This person designed the layout of maps, illustrations, and text so the book would look good.

Cover Design: George Turnbull, Cambridge, Massachusetts
Look at the cover of your book. The cover designer made it look the way it does.

Printed in: Denmark
by: Aarhus Stiftsbogtrykkerie
This printer was responsible for printing the pages and putting the book together inside a cover.

Paper
It is important to use a paper which is produced without dangerous chemicals which destroy the environment. This paper is bleached without poisonous chloride.

Typefaces
We use different "typefaces" to give typed letters different looks. In this book we have used: Univers Medium, **Bold,** **_Bold Italic_**, and Helvetica Regular, _Italic_ and **_Bold Italic_**.

Publisher: Interarts, Ltd., Cambridge, Massachusetts, U.S.A.
The publisher distributes the books to the schools and bookstores where you can buy them. To order more copies of this book, you can contact Interarts at 617-354-4655 or fax to them at 617-354-1476.

ISBN Number 1-879856-15-8
Each book printed in the world gets a special number to make it easier to find it in a library or bookstore.

Cartographer (Map Maker)_____
That's you! You put color on the world!
Good work!

INTERARTS

Maps International 1992

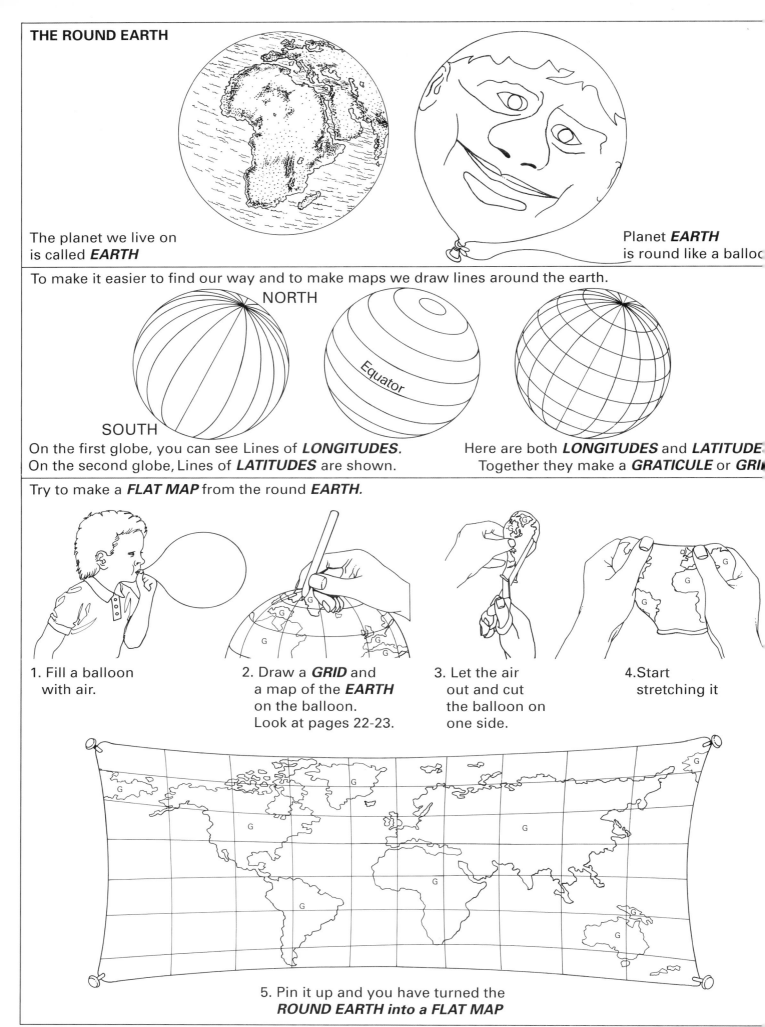

THE ROUND EARTH

The planet we live on
is called **EARTH**

Planet **EARTH**
is round like a balloo[n]

To make it easier to find our way and to make maps we draw lines around the earth.

NORTH

Equator

SOUTH

On the first globe, you can see Lines of **LONGITUDES**.
On the second globe, Lines of **LATITUDES** are shown.

Here are both **LONGITUDES** and **LATITUDE[S]**
Together they make a **GRATICULE** or **GRI[D]**

Try to make a **FLAT MAP** from the round **EARTH**.

1. Fill a balloon
with air.

2. Draw a **GRID** and
a map of the **EARTH**
on the balloon.
Look at pages 22-23.

3. Let the air
out and cut
the balloon on
one side.

4. Start
stretching it

5. Pin it up and you have turned the
ROUND EARTH into a FLAT MAP

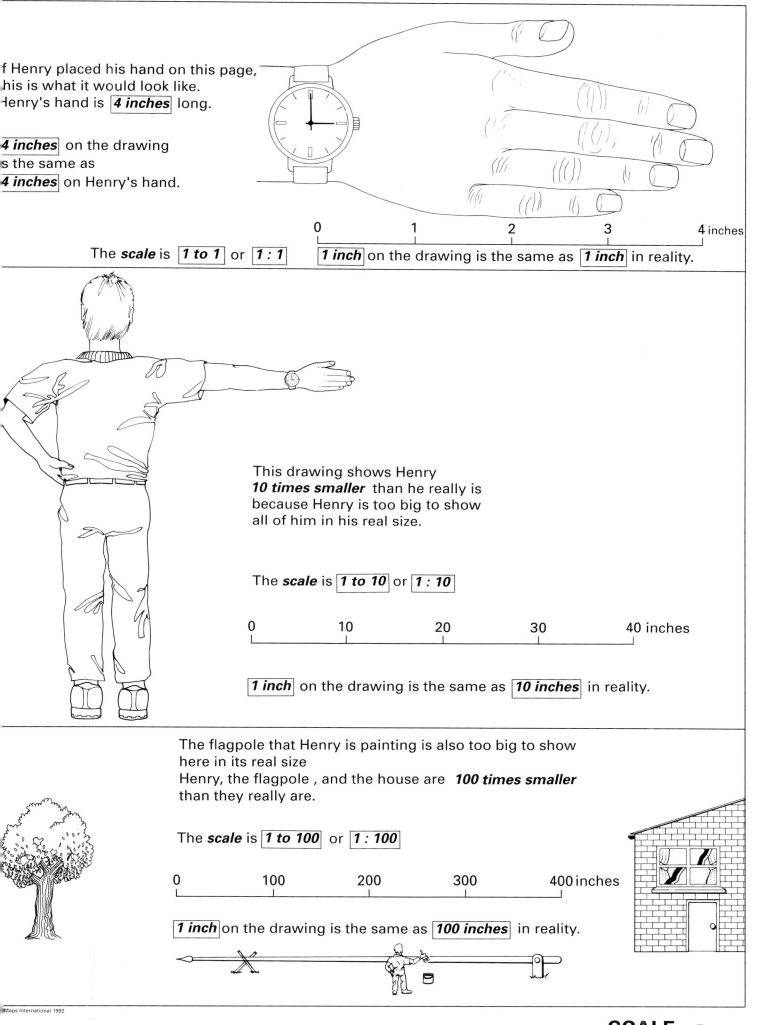

f Henry placed his hand on this page,
his is what it would look like.
Henry's hand is **4 inches** long.

4 inches on the drawing
s the same as
4 inches on Henry's hand.

0   1   2   3   4 inches

The **scale** is **1 to 1** or **1 : 1**   **1 inch** on the drawing is the same as **1 inch** in reality.

This drawing shows Henry
10 times smaller than he really is
because Henry is too big to show
all of him in his real size.

The **scale** is **1 to 10** or **1 : 10**

0   10   20   30   40 inches

1 inch on the drawing is the same as **10 inches** in reality.

The flagpole that Henry is painting is also too big to show
here in its real size
Henry, the flagpole , and the house are **100 times smaller**
than they really are.

The **scale** is **1 to 100** or **1 : 100**

0   100   200   300   400 inches

1 inch on the drawing is the same as **100 inches** in reality.

SCALE   Page 7

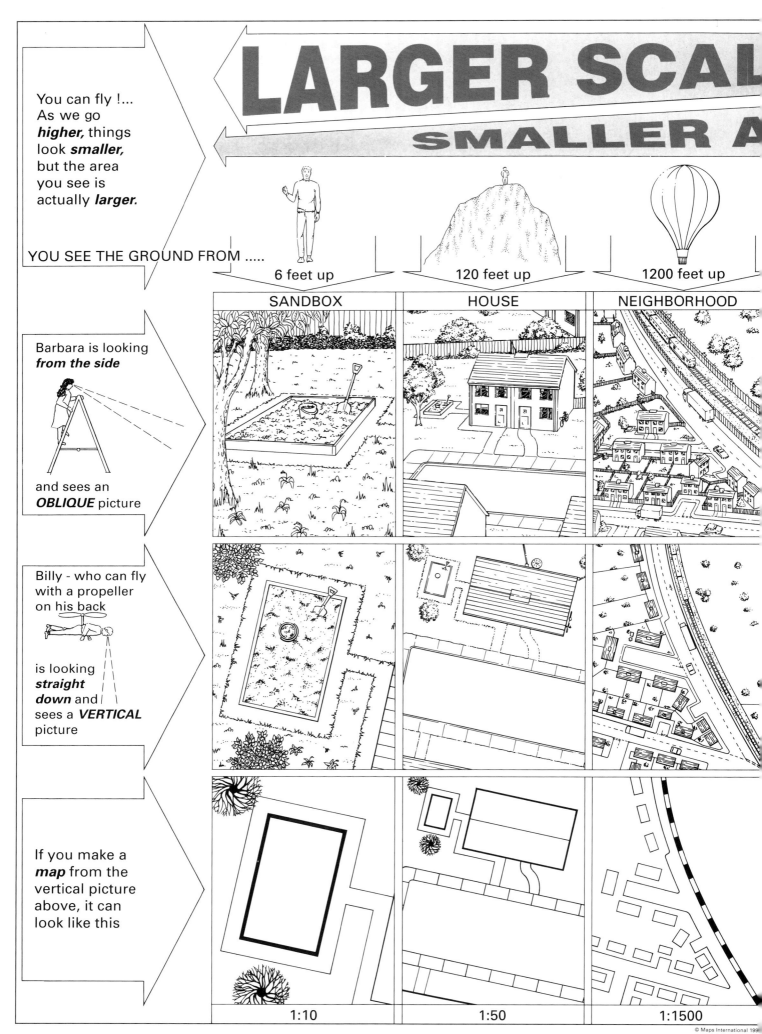

You can fly !... As we go **higher,** things look **smaller,** but the area you see is actually **larger.**

YOU SEE THE GROUND FROM .....

6 feet up | 120 feet up | 1200 feet up

SANDBOX | HOUSE | NEIGHBORHOOD

Barbara is looking **from the side** and sees an **OBLIQUE** picture

Billy - who can fly with a propeller on his back is looking **straight down** and sees a **VERTICAL** picture

If you make a **map** from the vertical picture above, it can look like this

1:10 | 1:50 | 1:1500

LARGER SCAL

SMALLER A

© Maps International 199

REA LARGER AREA

12000 feet up	36000 feet up	100+ miles up	200+ miles up

TOWN	REGION	EASTERN US	CONTINENT

| 1:15,000 | 1:500,000 | 1:40,000,000 | 1:120,000,000 |

Maps International 1992

Directions

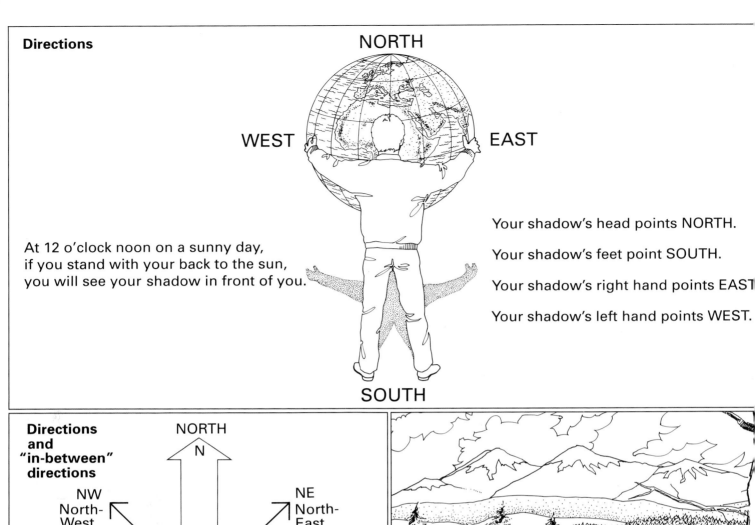

NORTH

WEST

EAST

At 12 o'clock noon on a sunny day,
if you stand with your back to the sun,
you will see your shadow in front of you.

Your shadow's head points NORTH.

Your shadow's feet point SOUTH.

Your shadow's right hand points EAST.

Your shadow's left hand points WEST.

SOUTH

Directions and "in-between" directions

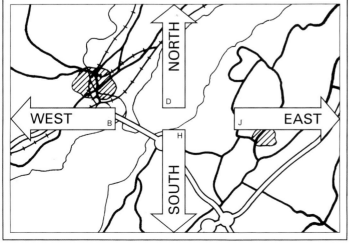

NORTH
N

NW
North-West

NE
North-East

D

W
WEST
B

E
EAST
J

H

SW
South-West

SE
South-East

S
SOUTH

On a map

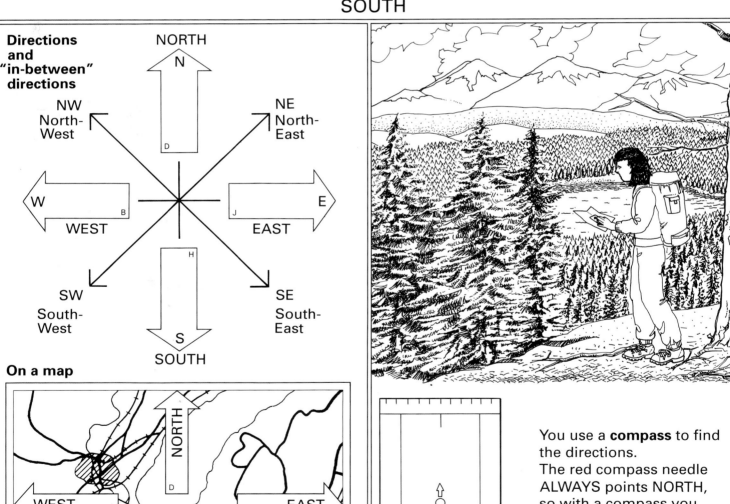

NORTH

D

WEST
B

EAST
J

H

SOUTH

You use a **compass** to find the directions.
The red compass needle ALWAYS points NORTH, so with a compass you can find your way in the forest or in the dark.

You have just found my treasure map

Follow the secret directions:

Start at X. Go one square NORTH, then one square EAST, then one square NORTH-EAST, then one square NORTH (BEWARE OF THE DRAGON), then two squares WEST, then one square NORTH-EAST (LOOK OUT FOR TRAPS), then three squares EAST, then five squares NORTH, then two squares WEST, then one square SOUTH-WEST, (KEEP YOUR BALANCE), then three squares SOUTH. The treasure is yours – if you took the right path!

CAPTAIN COOK'S TREASURE MAP Page 11

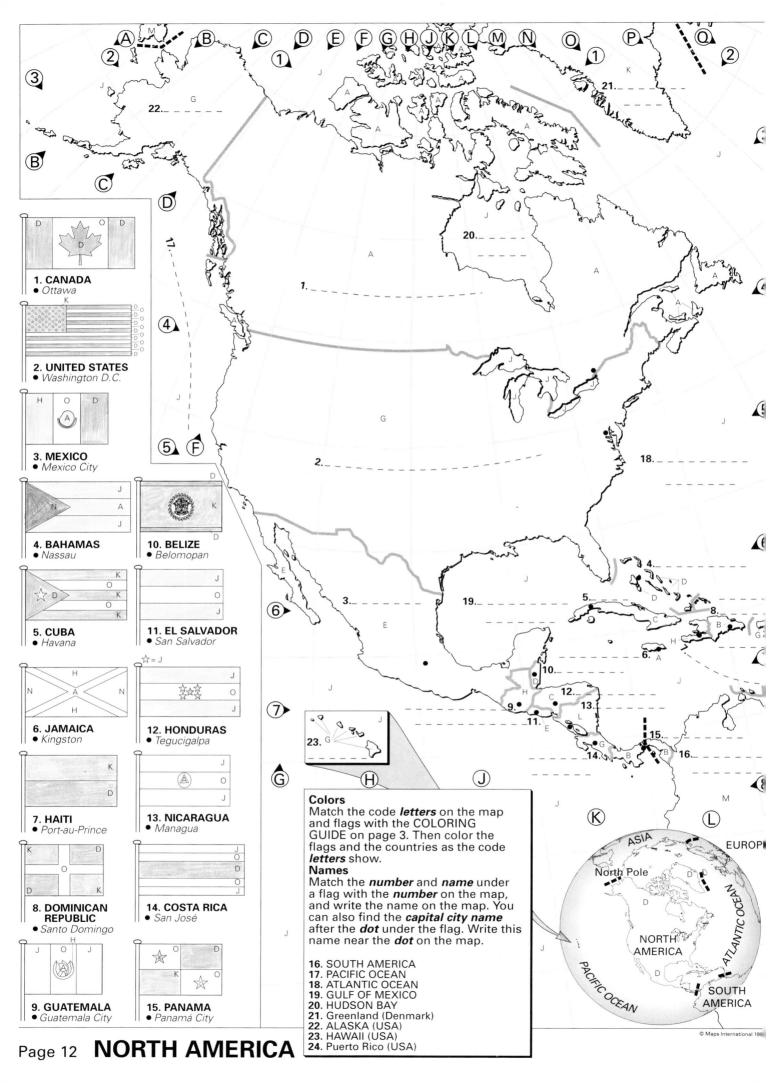

1. CANADA
● Ottawa

2. UNITED STATES
● Washington D.C.

3. MEXICO
● Mexico City

4. BAHAMAS
● Nassau

10. BELIZE
● Belomopan

5. CUBA
● Havana

11. EL SALVADOR
● San Salvador

6. JAMAICA
● Kingston

12. HONDURAS
● Tegucigalpa

7. HAITI
● Port-au-Prince

13. NICARAGUA
● Managua

8. DOMINICAN REPUBLIC
● Santo Domingo

14. COSTA RICA
● San José

9. GUATEMALA
● Guatemala City

15. PANAMA
● Panamá City

Colors
Match the code *letters* on the map and flags with the COLORING GUIDE on page 3. Then color the flags and the countries as the code *letters* show.

Names
Match the *number* and *name* under a flag with the *number* on the map, and write the name on the map. You can also find the *capital city name* after the *dot* under the flag. Write this name near the *dot* on the map.

16. SOUTH AMERICA
17. PACIFIC OCEAN
18. ATLANTIC OCEAN
19. GULF OF MEXICO
20. HUDSON BAY
21. Greenland (Denmark)
22. ALASKA (USA)
23. HAWAII (USA)
24. Puerto Rico (USA)

© Maps International 199

NORTH AMERICA

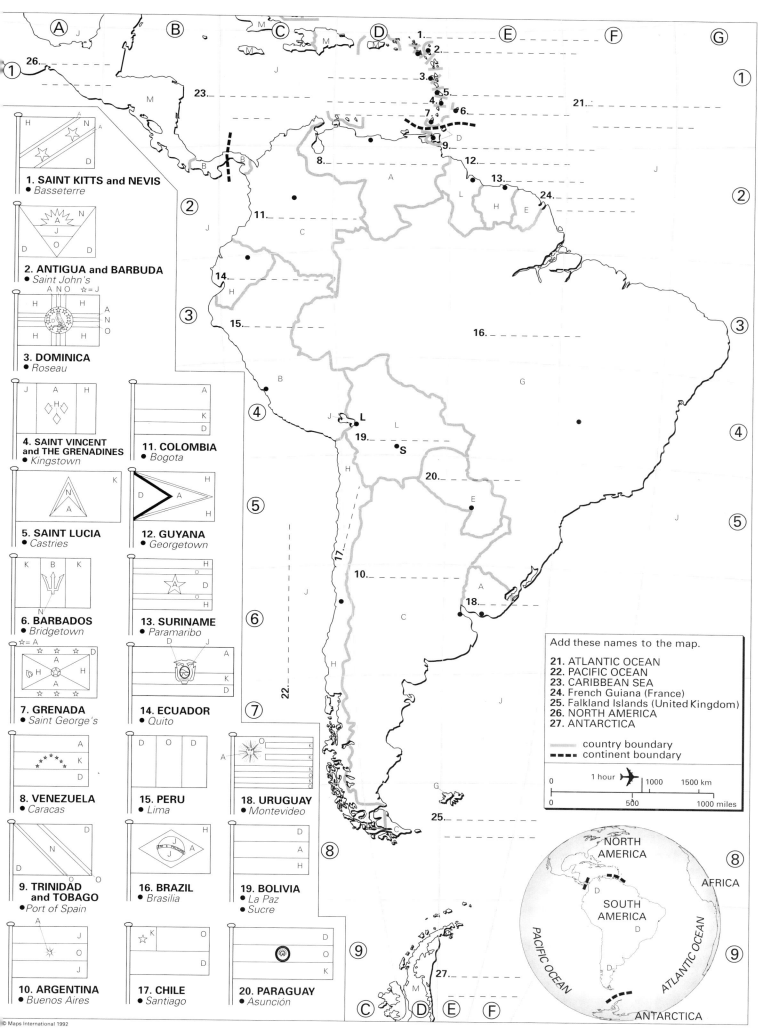

1. SAINT KITTS and NEVIS
● Basseterre

2. ANTIGUA and BARBUDA
● Saint John's

3. DOMINICA
● Roseau

4. SAINT VINCENT and THE GRENADINES
● Kingstown

5. SAINT LUCIA
● Castries

6. BARBADOS
● Bridgetown

7. GRENADA
● Saint George's

8. VENEZUELA
● Caracas

9. TRINIDAD and TOBAGO
● Port of Spain

10. ARGENTINA
● Buenos Aires

11. COLOMBIA
● Bogota

12. GUYANA
● Georgetown

13. SURINAME
● Paramaribo

14. ECUADOR
● Quito

15. PERU
● Lima

16. BRAZIL
● Brasilia

17. CHILE
● Santiago

18. URUGUAY
● Montevideo

19. BOLIVIA
● La Paz
● Sucre

20. PARAGUAY
● Asunción

Add these names to the map.

21. ATLANTIC OCEAN
22. PACIFIC OCEAN
23. CARIBBEAN SEA
24. French Guiana (France)
25. Falkland Islands (United Kingdom)
26. NORTH AMERICA
27. ANTARCTICA

country boundary
━ ━ ━ continent boundary

0   1 hour ✈   1000   1500 km
0   500   1000 miles

NORTH AMERICA
SOUTH AMERICA
AFRICA
PACIFIC OCEAN
ATLANTIC OCEAN
ANTARCTICA

© Maps International 1992

SOUTH AMERICA Page 13

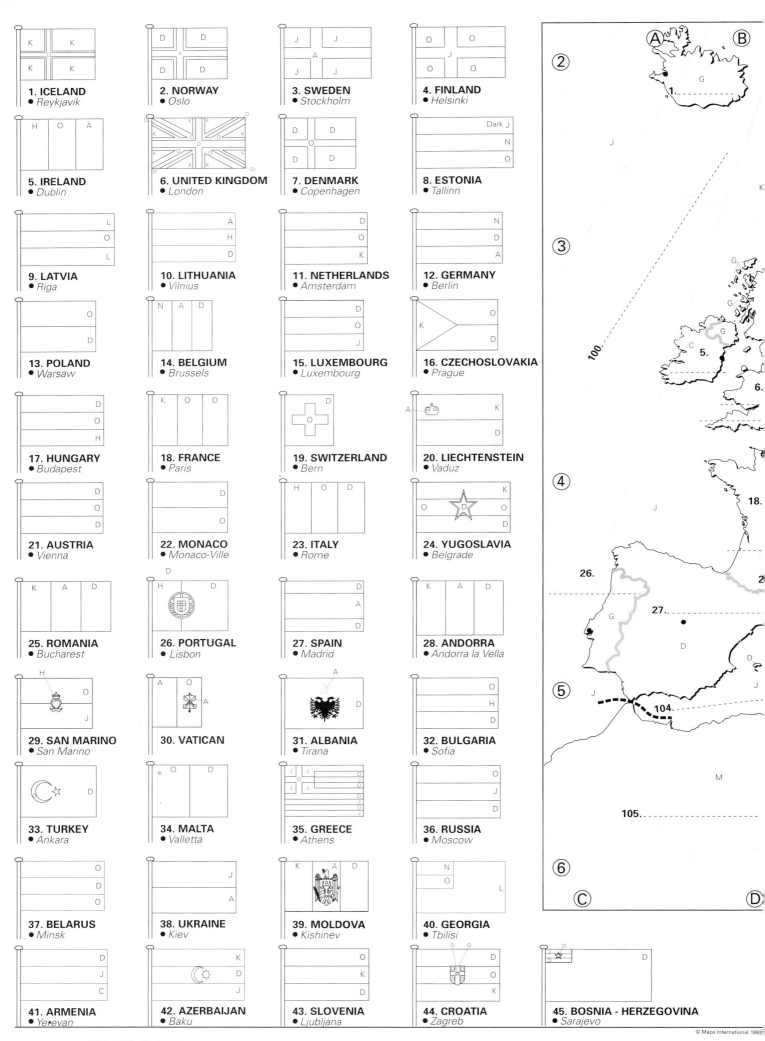

1. ICELAND
● Reykjavik

2. NORWAY
● Oslo

3. SWEDEN
● Stockholm

4. FINLAND
● Helsinki

5. IRELAND
● Dublin

6. UNITED KINGDOM
● London

7. DENMARK
● Copenhagen

8. ESTONIA
● Tallinn

9. LATVIA
● Riga

10. LITHUANIA
● Vilnius

11. NETHERLANDS
● Amsterdam

12. GERMANY
● Berlin

13. POLAND
● Warsaw

14. BELGIUM
● Brussels

15. LUXEMBOURG
● Luxembourg

16. CZECHOSLOVAKIA
● Prague

17. HUNGARY
● Budapest

18. FRANCE
● Paris

19. SWITZERLAND
● Bern

20. LIECHTENSTEIN
● Vaduz

21. AUSTRIA
● Vienna

22. MONACO
● Monaco-Ville

23. ITALY
● Rome

24. YUGOSLAVIA
● Belgrade

25. ROMANIA
● Bucharest

26. PORTUGAL
● Lisbon

27. SPAIN
● Madrid

28. ANDORRA
● Andorra la Vella

29. SAN MARINO
● San Marino

30. VATICAN

31. ALBANIA
● Tirana

32. BULGARIA
● Sofia

33. TURKEY
● Ankara

34. MALTA
● Valletta

35. GREECE
● Athens

36. RUSSIA
● Moscow

37. BELARUS
● Minsk

38. UKRAINE
● Kiev

39. MOLDOVA
● Kishinev

40. GEORGIA
● Tbilisi

41. ARMENIA
● Yerevan

42. AZERBAIJAN
● Baku

43. SLOVENIA
● Ljubljana

44. CROATIA
● Zagreb

45. BOSNIA - HERZEGOVINA
● Sarajevo

© Maps International 1992

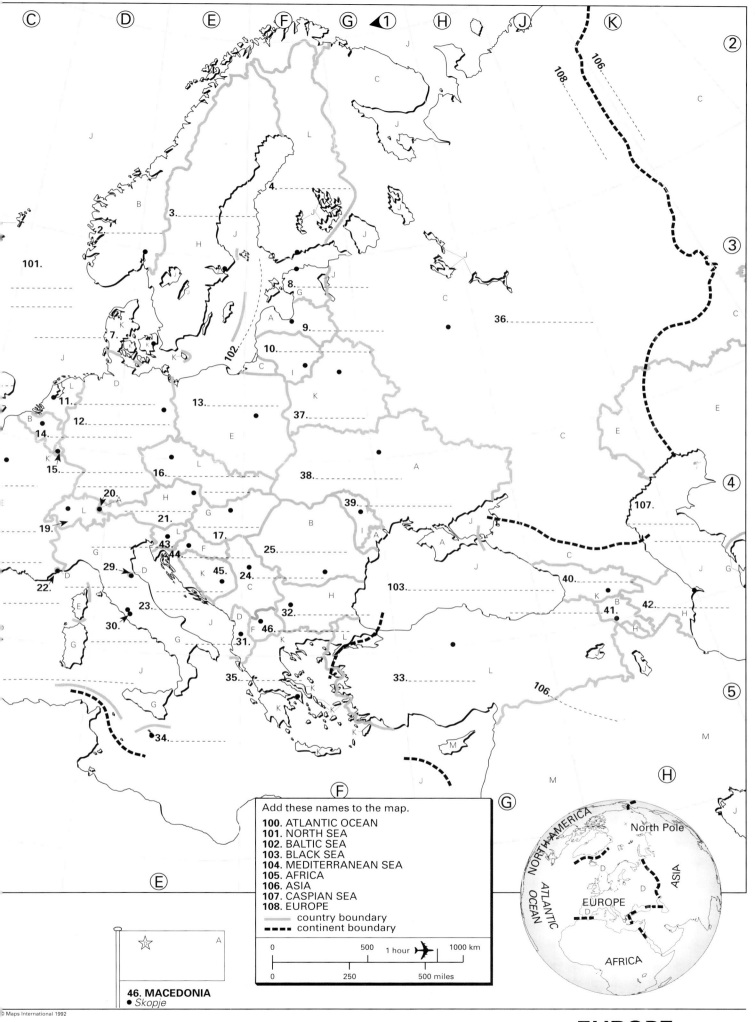

Add these names to the map.

100. ATLANTIC OCEAN
101. NORTH SEA
102. BALTIC SEA
103. BLACK SEA
104. MEDITERRANEAN SEA
105. AFRICA
106. ASIA
107. CASPIAN SEA
108. EUROPE

━━━ country boundary
▬ ▬ ▬ continent boundary

| 0 | | 500 | 1 hour ✈ | 1000 km |

| 0 | 250 | 500 miles |

46. MACEDONIA
● Skopje

© Maps International 1992

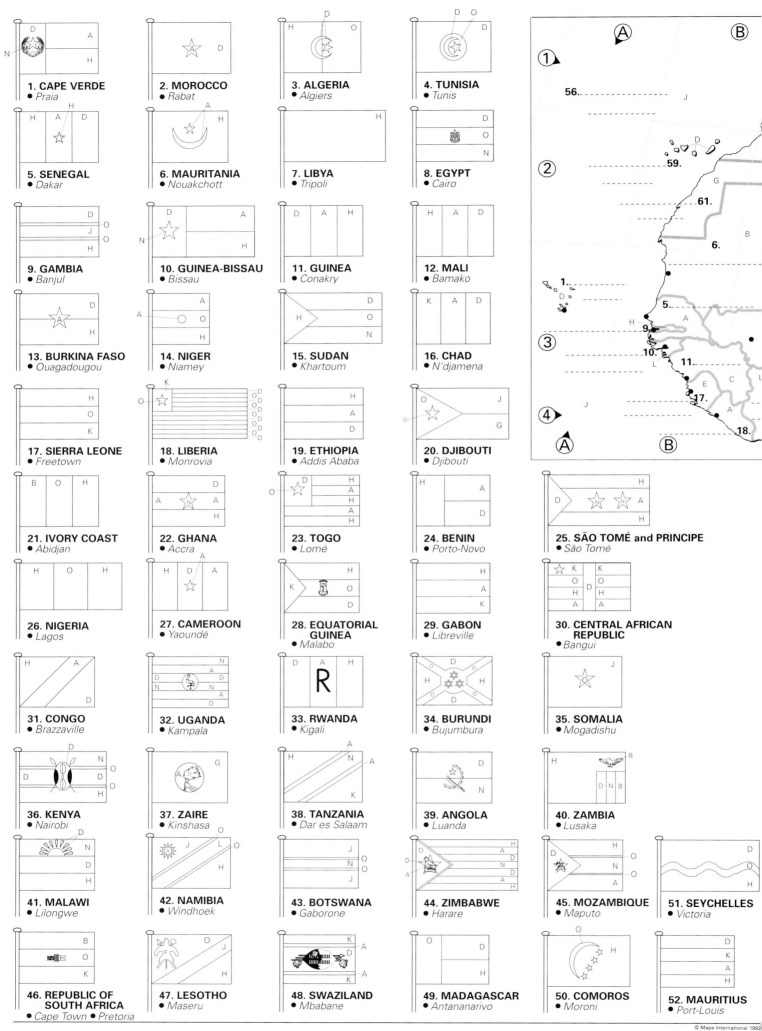

1. CAPE VERDE
● Praia

2. MOROCCO
● Rabat

3. ALGERIA
● Algiers

4. TUNISIA
● Tunis

5. SENEGAL
● Dakar

6. MAURITANIA
● Nouakchott

7. LIBYA
● Tripoli

8. EGYPT
● Cairo

9. GAMBIA
● Banjul

10. GUINEA-BISSAU
● Bissau

11. GUINEA
● Conakry

12. MALI
● Bamako

13. BURKINA FASO
● Ouagadougou

14. NIGER
● Niamey

15. SUDAN
● Khartoum

16. CHAD
● N'djamena

17. SIERRA LEONE
● Freetown

18. LIBERIA
● Monrovia

19. ETHIOPIA
● Addis Ababa

20. DJIBOUTI
● Djibouti

21. IVORY COAST
● Abidjan

22. GHANA
● Accra

23. TOGO
● Lomé

24. BENIN
● Porto-Novo

25. SÃO TOMÉ and PRINCIPE
● São Tomé

26. NIGERIA
● Lagos

27. CAMEROON
● Yaoundé

28. EQUATORIAL GUINEA
● Malabo

29. GABON
● Libreville

30. CENTRAL AFRICAN REPUBLIC
● Bangui

31. CONGO
● Brazzaville

32. UGANDA
● Kampala

33. RWANDA
● Kigali

34. BURUNDI
● Bujumbura

35. SOMALIA
● Mogadishu

36. KENYA
● Nairobi

37. ZAIRE
● Kinshasa

38. TANZANIA
● Dar es Salaam

39. ANGOLA
● Luanda

40. ZAMBIA
● Lusaka

41. MALAWI
● Lilongwe

42. NAMIBIA
● Windhoek

43. BOTSWANA
● Gaborone

44. ZIMBABWE
● Harare

45. MOZAMBIQUE
● Maputo

51. SEYCHELLES
● Victoria

46. REPUBLIC OF SOUTH AFRICA
● Cape Town ● Pretoria

47. LESOTHO
● Maseru

48. SWAZILAND
● Mbabane

49. MADAGASCAR
● Antananarivo

50. COMOROS
● Moroni

52. MAURITIUS
● Port-Louis

© Maps International 1992

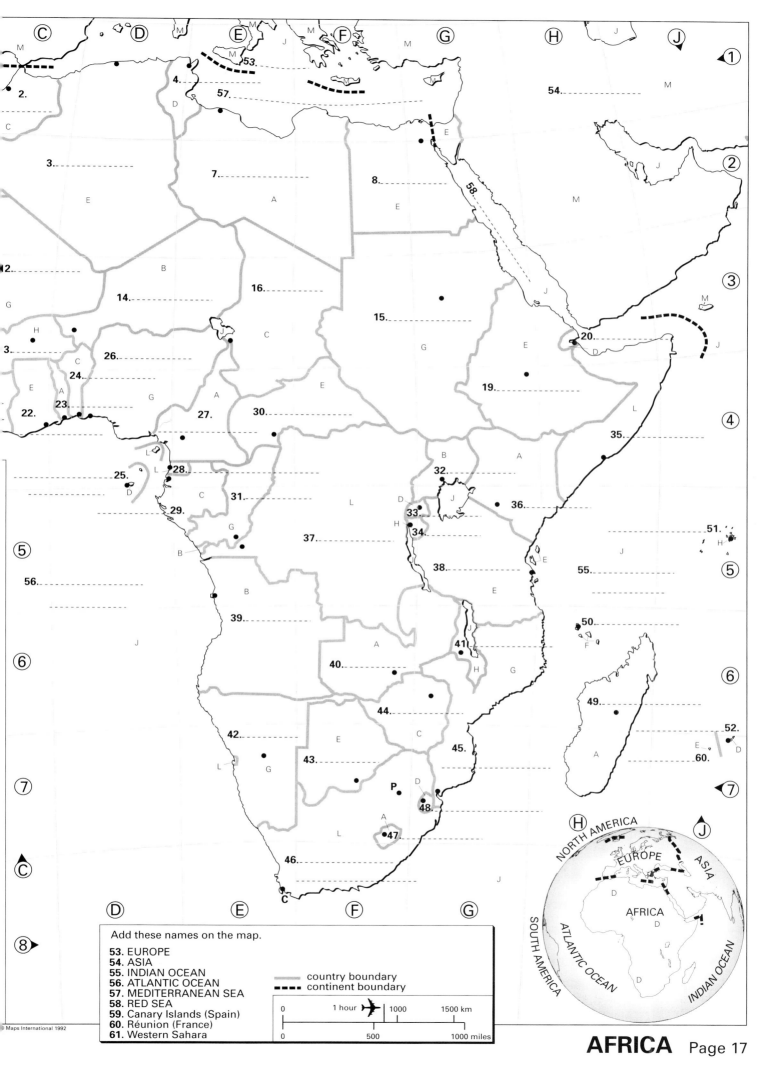

AFRICA Page 17

Add these names on the map.

53. EUROPE
54. ASIA
55. INDIAN OCEAN
56. ATLANTIC OCEAN
57. MEDITERRANEAN SEA
58. RED SEA
59. Canary Islands (Spain)
60. Réunion (France)
61. Western Sahara

—— country boundary
▪▪▪ continent boundary

0   1 hour ✈   1000   1500 km
0   500   1000 miles

© Maps International 1992

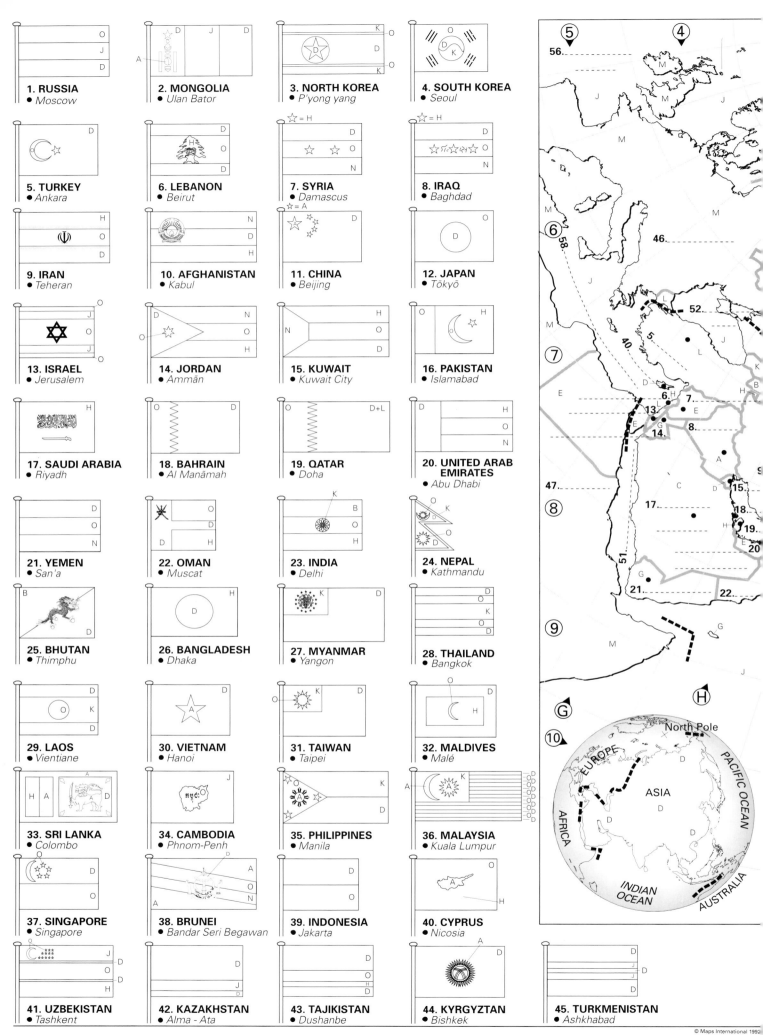

1. RUSSIA
● Moscow

2. MONGOLIA
● Ulan Bator

3. NORTH KOREA
● P'yong yang

4. SOUTH KOREA
● Seoul

5. TURKEY
● Ankara

6. LEBANON
● Beirut

7. SYRIA
● Damascus

8. IRAQ
● Baghdad

9. IRAN
● Teheran

10. AFGHANISTAN
● Kabul

11. CHINA
● Beijing

12. JAPAN
● Tōkyō

13. ISRAEL
● Jerusalem

14. JORDAN
● Ammān

15. KUWAIT
● Kuwait City

16. PAKISTAN
● Islamabad

17. SAUDI ARABIA
● Riyadh

18. BAHRAIN
● Al Manāmah

19. QATAR
● Doha

20. UNITED ARAB EMIRATES
● Abu Dhabi

21. YEMEN
● San'a

22. OMAN
● Muscat

23. INDIA
● Delhi

24. NEPAL
● Kathmandu

25. BHUTAN
● Thimphu

26. BANGLADESH
● Dhaka

27. MYANMAR
● Yangon

28. THAILAND
● Bangkok

29. LAOS
● Vientiane

30. VIETNAM
● Hanoi

31. TAIWAN
● Taipei

32. MALDIVES
● Malé

33. SRI LANKA
● Colombo

34. CAMBODIA
● Phnom-Penh

35. PHILIPPINES
● Manila

36. MALAYSIA
● Kuala Lumpur

37. SINGAPORE
● Singapore

38. BRUNEI
● Bandar Seri Begawan

39. INDONESIA
● Jakarta

40. CYPRUS
● Nicosia

41. UZBEKISTAN
● Tashkent

42. KAZAKHSTAN
● Alma - Ata

43. TAJIKISTAN
● Dushanbe

44. KYRGYZTAN
● Bishkek

45. TURKMENISTAN
● Ashkhabad

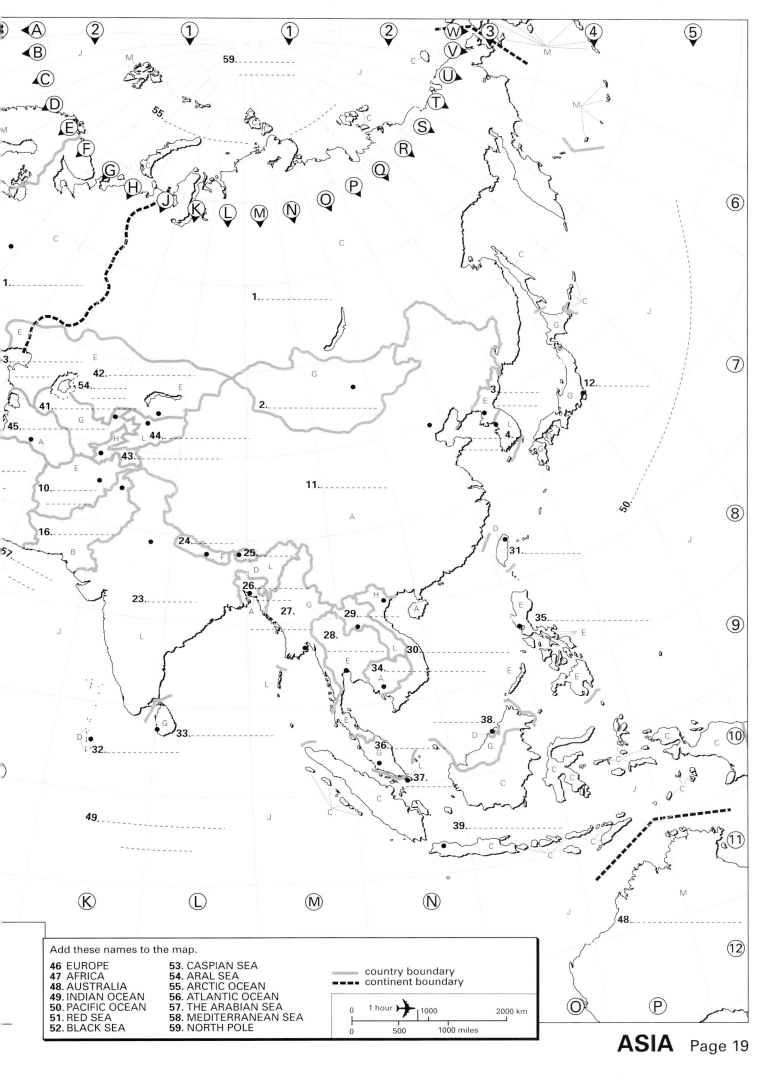

Add these names to the map.

46 EUROPE	**53.** CASPIAN SEA
47 AFRICA	**54.** ARAL SEA
48. AUSTRALIA	**55.** ARCTIC OCEAN
49. INDIAN OCEAN	**56.** ATLANTIC OCEAN
50. PACIFIC OCEAN	**57.** THE ARABIAN SEA
51. RED SEA	**58.** MEDITERRANEAN SEA
52. BLACK SEA	**59.** NORTH POLE

country boundary
continent boundary

0   1 hour ✈ 1000   2000 km
0   500   1000 miles

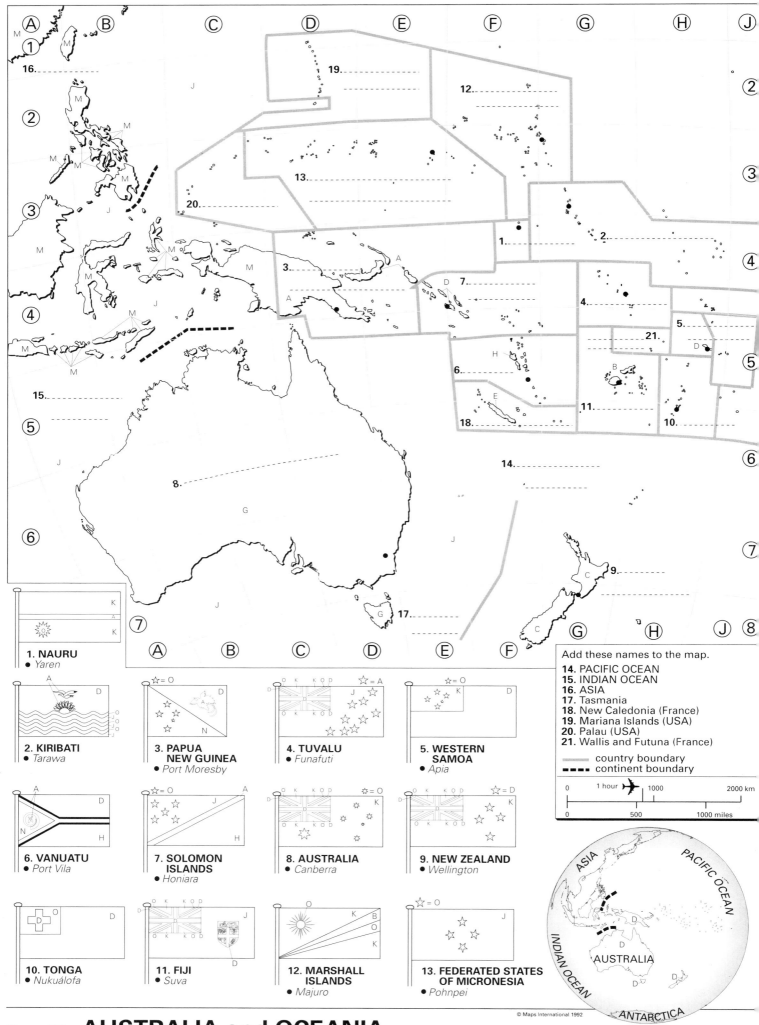

© Maps International 1992

Add these names to the map.

14. PACIFIC OCEAN
15. INDIAN OCEAN
16. ASIA
17. Tasmania
18. New Caledonia (France)
19. Mariana Islands (USA)
20. Palau (USA)
21. Wallis and Futuna (France)

country boundary
continent boundary

0   1 hour   1000   2000 km

0   500   1000 miles

1. NAURU
● Yaren

2. KIRIBATI
● Tarawa

3. PAPUA NEW GUINEA
● Port Moresby

4. TUVALU
● Funafuti

5. WESTERN SAMOA
● Apia

6. VANUATU
● Port Vila

7. SOLOMON ISLANDS
● Honiara

8. AUSTRALIA
● Canberra

9. NEW ZEALAND
● Wellington

10. TONGA
● Nukuálofa

11. FIJI
● Suva

12. MARSHALL ISLANDS
● Majuro

13. FEDERATED STATES OF MICRONESIA
● Pohnpei

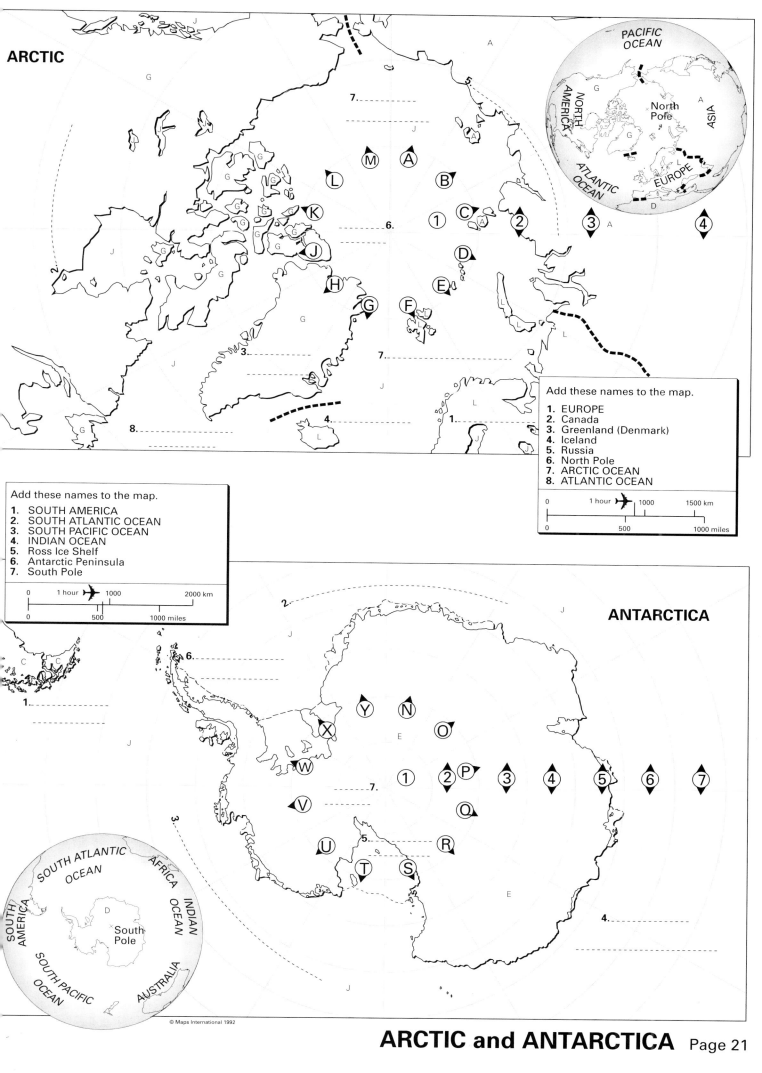

ARCTIC

Add these names to the map.

1. EUROPE
2. Canada
3. Greenland (Denmark)
4. Iceland
5. Russia
6. North Pole
7. ARCTIC OCEAN
8. ATLANTIC OCEAN

Add these names to the map.

1. SOUTH AMERICA
2. SOUTH ATLANTIC OCEAN
3. SOUTH PACIFIC OCEAN
4. INDIAN OCEAN
5. Ross Ice Shelf
6. Antarctic Peninsula
7. South Pole

ANTARCTICA

© Maps International 1992

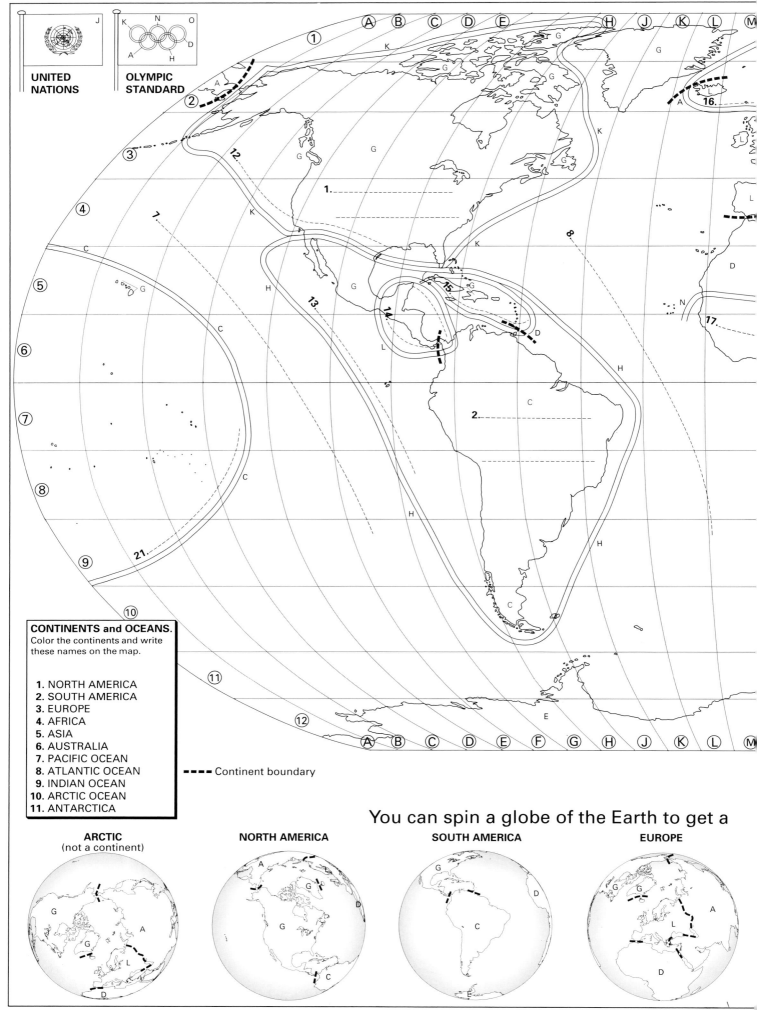

UNITED NATIONS

OLYMPIC STANDARD

CONTINENTS and OCEANS.
Color the continents and write these names on the map.

1. NORTH AMERICA
2. SOUTH AMERICA
3. EUROPE
4. AFRICA
5. ASIA
6. AUSTRALIA
7. PACIFIC OCEAN
8. ATLANTIC OCEAN
9. INDIAN OCEAN
10. ARCTIC OCEAN
11. ANTARCTICA

▪ ▪ ▪ Continent boundary

You can spin a globe of the Earth to get a

ARCTIC
(not a continent)

NORTH AMERICA

SOUTH AMERICA

EUROPE

© Maps International 1992

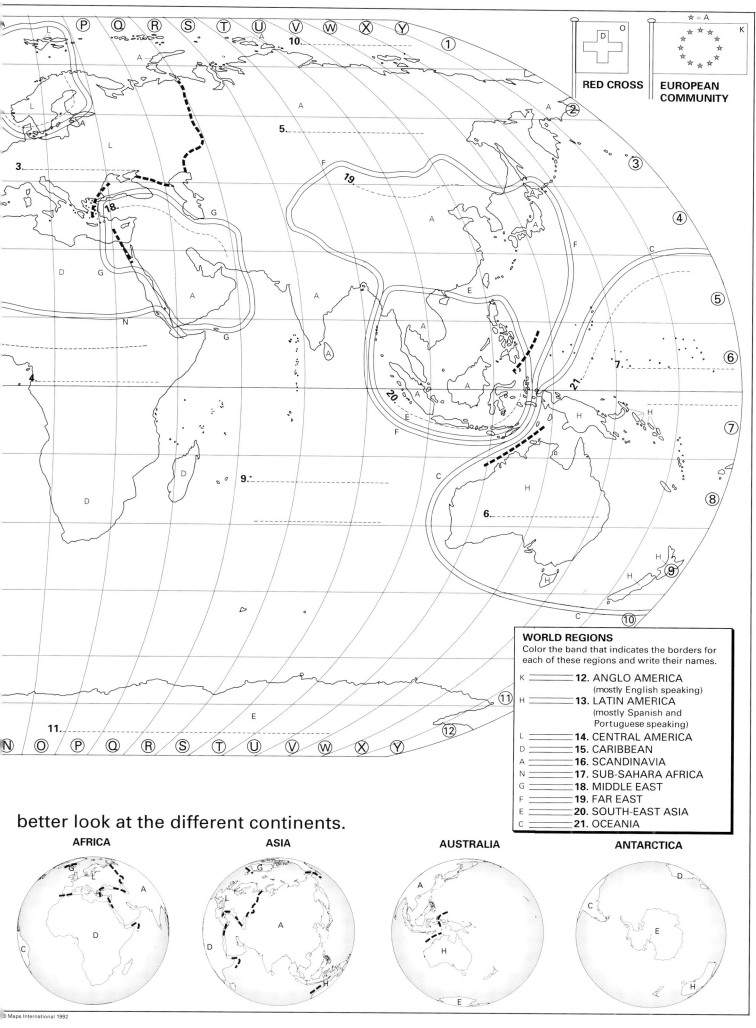

RED CROSS

EUROPEAN COMMUNITY

☆ = A

WORLD REGIONS
Color the band that indicates the borders for each of these regions and write their names.

K ————— **12.** ANGLO AMERICA
(mostly English speaking)
H ————— **13.** LATIN AMERICA
(mostly Spanish and Portuguese speaking)
L ————— **14.** CENTRAL AMERICA
D ————— **15.** CARIBBEAN
A ————— **16.** SCANDINAVIA
N ————— **17.** SUB-SAHARA AFRICA
G ————— **18.** MIDDLE EAST
F ————— **19.** FAR EAST
E ————— **20.** SOUTH-EAST ASIA
C ————— **21.** OCEANIA

better look at the different continents.

AFRICA   **ASIA**   **AUSTRALIA**   **ANTARCTICA**

© Maps International 1992

Page 23

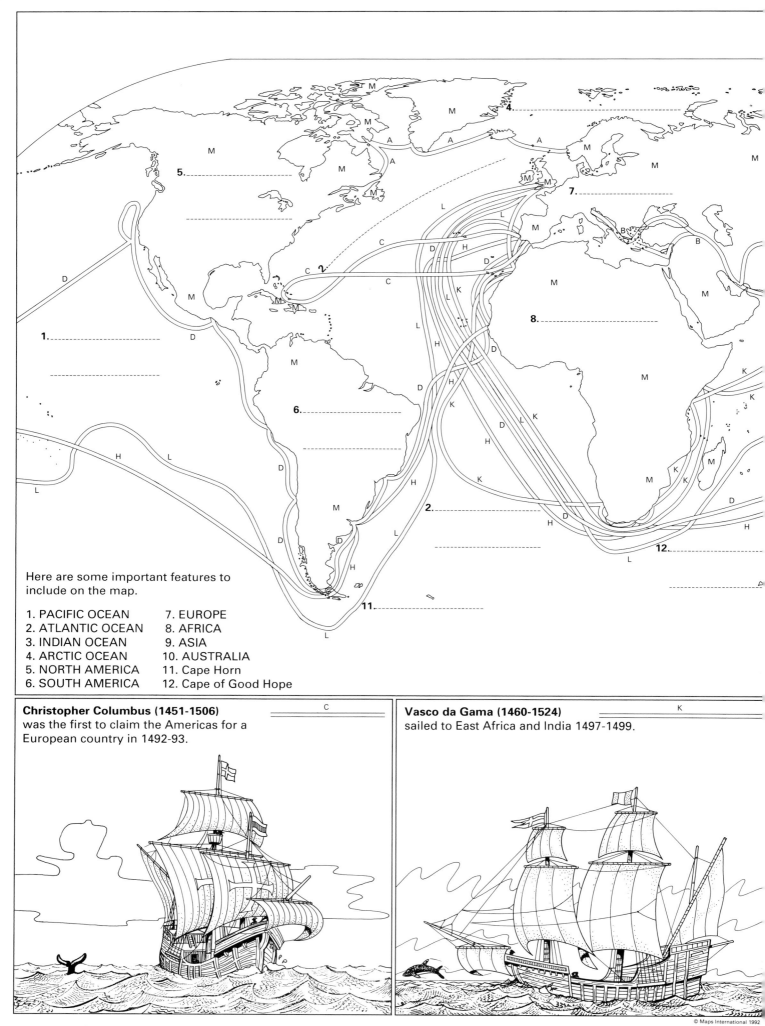

Here are some important features to include on the map.

1. PACIFIC OCEAN
2. ATLANTIC OCEAN
3. INDIAN OCEAN
4. ARCTIC OCEAN
5. NORTH AMERICA
6. SOUTH AMERICA
7. EUROPE
8. AFRICA
9. ASIA
10. AUSTRALIA
11. Cape Horn
12. Cape of Good Hope

Christopher Columbus (1451-1506) was the first to claim the Americas for a European country in 1492-93.

Vasco da Gama (1460-1524) sailed to East Africa and India 1497-1499.

© Maps International 1992

The viking **Leif Eriksson** is believed to have sailed to Iceland, Greenland and Newfoundland in about the year 1000.

James Cook (1728-79) was the first person from Europe known to have landed in Australia.

Francis Drake (1545-1596) was a pirate working for the Queen of England. He was the first English sailor to sail around the world from 1577-1580.

Follow These Famous Explorers.
Find the color coded route on the map that matches the color code next to the explorer's name. Then navigate the world as each of the explorers did by coloring in their routes on the map.

Ferdinand Magellan (1480-1521) explored South America from 1519-21. His ship returned to Spain in 1522 after the first trip around the world.

Marco Polo (1254-1324) went overland from Italy to China from 1271-95, and returned.

© Maps International 1992

Page 25

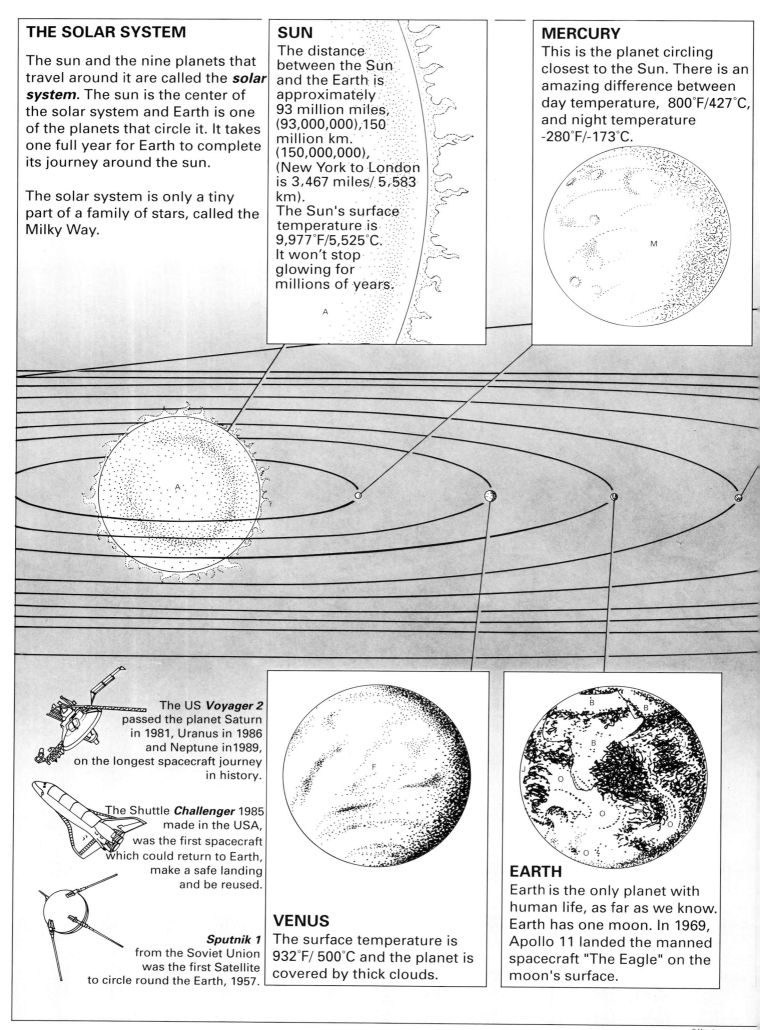

THE SOLAR SYSTEM

The sun and the nine planets that travel around it are called the **solar system.** The sun is the center of the solar system and Earth is one of the planets that circle it. It takes one full year for Earth to complete its journey around the sun.

The solar system is only a tiny part of a family of stars, called the Milky Way.

SUN

The distance between the Sun and the Earth is approximately 93 million miles, (93,000,000),150 million km. (150,000,000), (New York to London is 3,467 miles/ 5,583 km). The Sun's surface temperature is 9,977°F/5,525°C. It won't stop glowing for millions of years.

A

MERCURY

This is the planet circling closest to the Sun. There is an amazing difference between day temperature, 800°F/427°C, and night temperature -280°F/-173°C.

The US *Voyager 2* passed the planet Saturn in 1981, Uranus in 1986 and Neptune in1989, on the longest spacecraft journey in history.

The Shuttle *Challenger* 1985 made in the USA, was the first spacecraft which could return to Earth, make a safe landing and be reused.

Sputnik 1 from the Soviet Union was the first Satellite to circle round the Earth, 1957.

VENUS

The surface temperature is 932°F/ 500°C and the planet is covered by thick clouds.

EARTH

Earth is the only planet with human life, as far as we know. Earth has one moon. In 1969, Apollo 11 landed the manned spacecraft "The Eagle" on the moon's surface.

MARS
This planet has a reddish color and two white polar regions; Mars has two small moons. In 1976 an unmanned spacecraft landed on Mars.

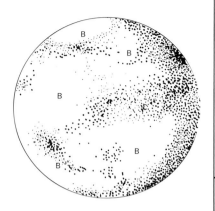

SATURN
Surrounded by a huge ring-system, this planet has at least 22 moons. In September 1979 the spacecraft Pioneer II passed at a distance of 13,290 miles/ 21,700 km and took excellent "close-up" photos.

PLUTO
Known as the outermost planet Pluto is 3.75 billion miles/ 6 billion km from the Sun. It has one known moon, Charon. Pluto was discovered as late as 1930.

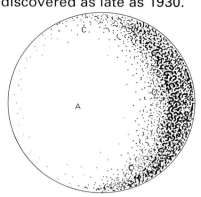

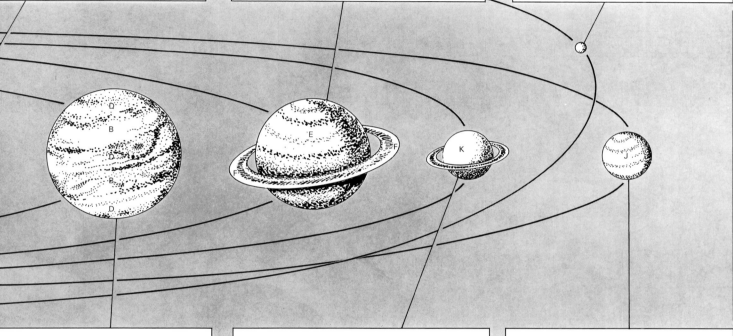

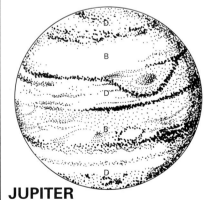

JUPITER
This is the largest planet and has at least 17 moons, 14 have been observed from Earth so far. The first four moons were discovered by Galileo in the year 1610.

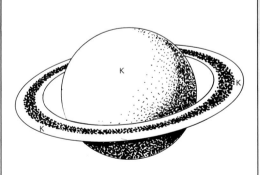

URANUS
Discovered in 1781, it has at least 15 moons. In 1977 it was found that Uranus has a ring-system.

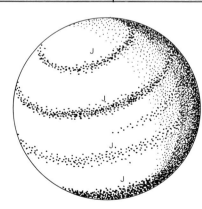

NEPTUNE
This planet was discovered in 1846, and it has eight moons. The largest moon is called Triton.

Our planet spins on its own axis one full turn in 24 hours, which is one day and one night.
When one side of the planet is facing the sun, the sun can shine on that side, so that half of the planet has *daytime.* The other side of the planet is in shadow and so that side has *nighttime.*

The Earth has been divided into 24 roughly equal *time zones.* If you think of the round Earth as being shaped like this tube with grids, you can picture how the time zone is figured for different parts of the Earth.

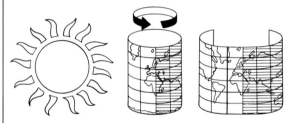

Color the time zones and see which parts of the Earth have the same time you have. Also try to figure out which places have night when you have day. When you have made your own globe (page 41) you can try this activity with a flashlight.

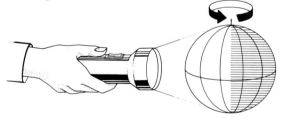

There is one line of longitude called the **Greenwich Meridian** which runs through the Greenwich Observatory near London. From this line at 0° all other lines of longitude are numbered and all other time zones are measured. Half way around the world from Greenwich is the **International Date Line** at 180° of longitude. This is where the time changes from one day to another.

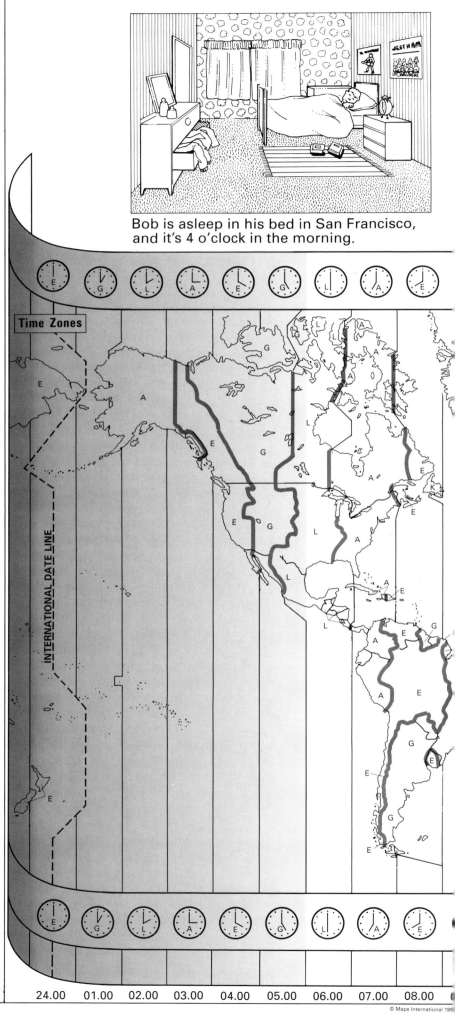

Bob is asleep in his bed in San Francisco, and it's 4 o'clock in the morning.

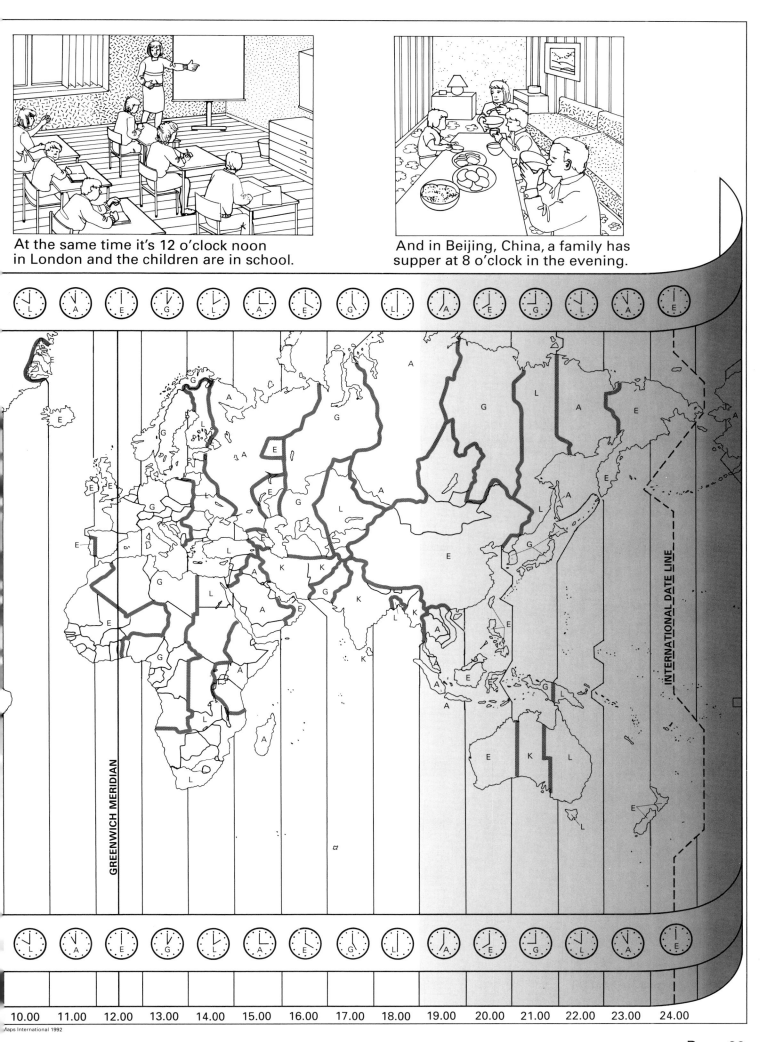

At the same time it's 12 o'clock noon in London and the children are in school.

And in Beijing, China, a family has supper at 8 o'clock in the evening.

GREENWICH MERIDIAN

INTERNATIONAL DATE LINE

| 10.00 | 11.00 | 12.00 | 13.00 | 14.00 | 15.00 | 16.00 | 17.00 | 18.00 | 19.00 | 20.00 | 21.00 | 22.00 | 23.00 | 24.00 |

Maps International 1992

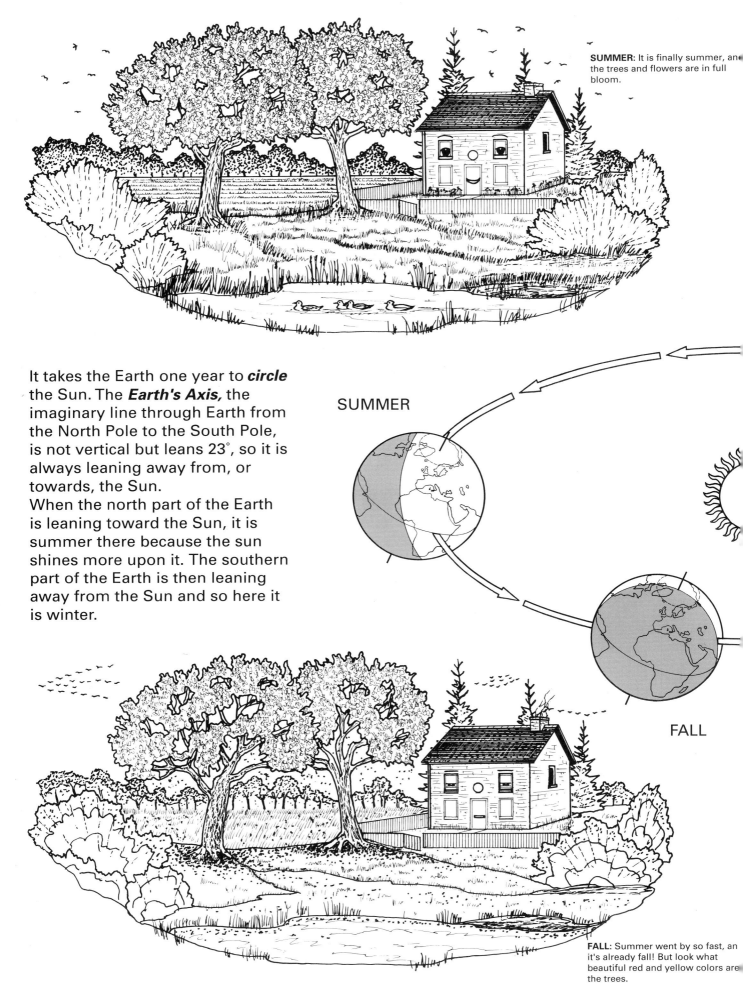

SUMMER: It is finally summer, and the trees and flowers are in full bloom.

SUMMER

It takes the Earth one year to *circle* the Sun. The ***Earth's Axis,*** the imaginary line through Earth from the North Pole to the South Pole, is not vertical but leans 23°, so it is always leaning away from, or towards, the Sun.

When the north part of the Earth is leaning toward the Sun, it is summer there because the sun shines more upon it. The southern part of the Earth is then leaning away from the Sun and so here it is winter.

FALL

FALL: Summer went by so fast, and it's already fall! But look what beautiful red and yellow colors are the trees.

© Maps International 19

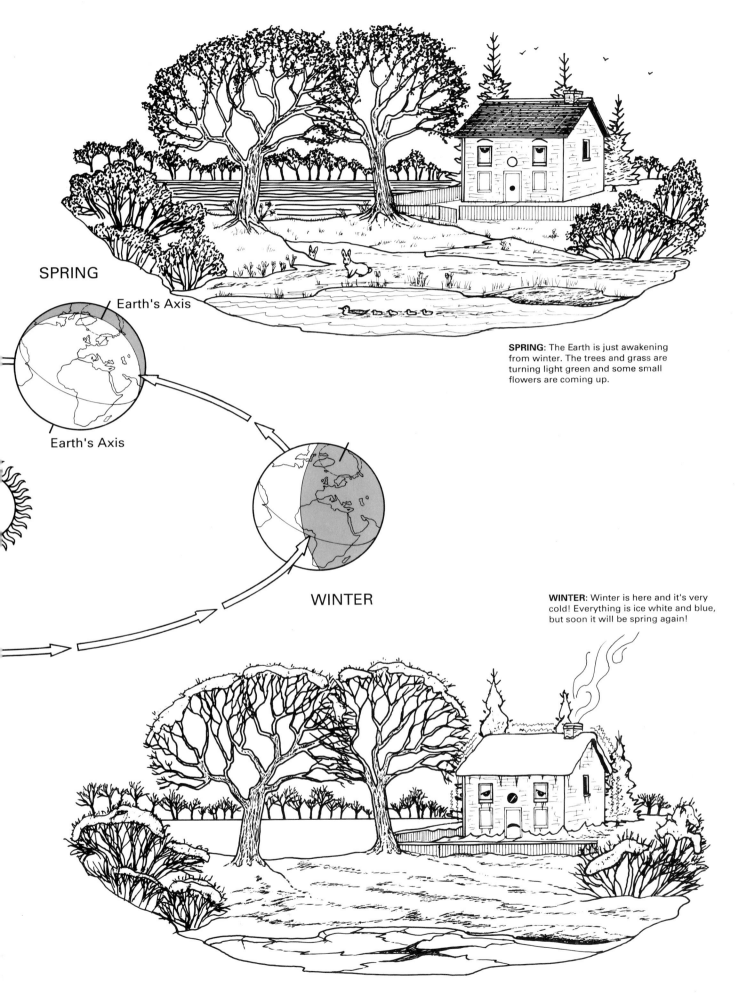

SPRING

Earth's Axis

Earth's Axis

WINTER

SPRING: The Earth is just awakening from winter. The trees and grass are turning light green and some small flowers are coming up.

WINTER: Winter is here and it's very cold! Everything is ice white and blue, but soon it will be spring again!

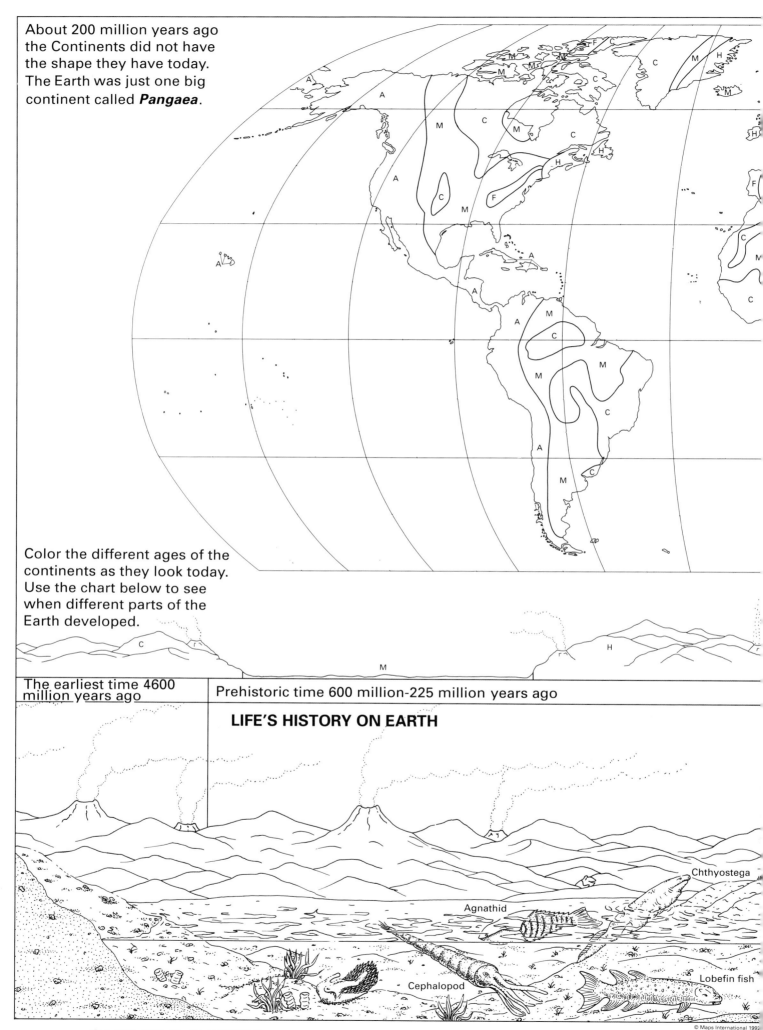

About 200 million years ago the Continents did not have the shape they have today. The Earth was just one big continent called **Pangaea**.

Color the different ages of the continents as they look today. Use the chart below to see when different parts of the Earth developed.

The earliest time 4600 million years ago	Prehistoric time 600 million-225 million years ago

LIFE'S HISTORY ON EARTH

Chthyostega

Agnathid

Cephalopod

Lobefin fish

© Maps International 1992

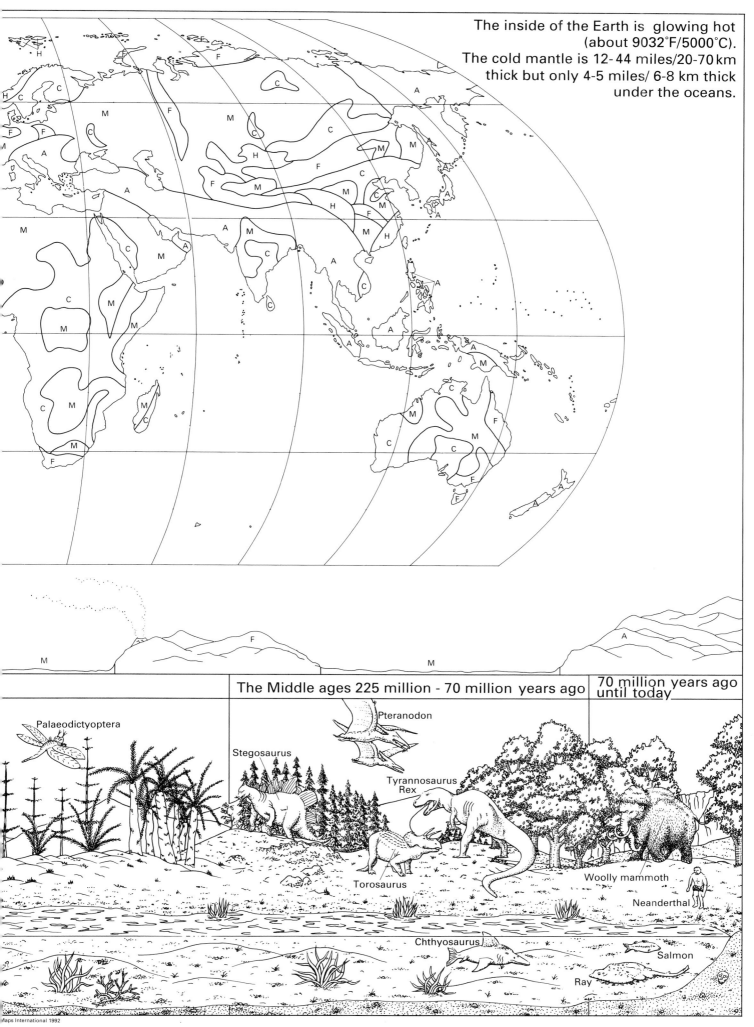

The inside of the Earth is glowing hot (about 9032°F/5000°C). The cold mantle is 12-44 miles/20-70 km thick but only 4-5 miles/ 6-8 km thick under the oceans.

The Middle ages 225 million - 70 million years ago

70 million years ago until today

Palaeodictyoptera

Pteranodon

Stegosaurus

Tyrannosaurus Rex

Torosaurus

Woolly mammoth

Neanderthal

Chthyosaurus

Salmon

Ray

Maps International 1992

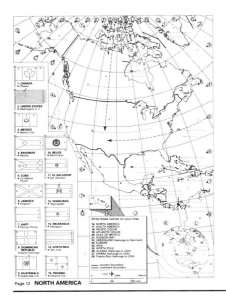

This is an INDEX of all the names you have written in your MapBook. The names are listed in alphabetical order to make it easy to find them.

For example:-
Look for the UNITED STATES in the index. Have you found **UNITED STATES 12 H 5**? **12** means that you'll find the UNITED STATES on page **12**.

Turn to page **12**
At the top and bottom of page **12** you find the letters A to Q. Along the left and right sides of the map are the numbers 1 to 8.

Find the **H** at the top of the page and go down between the thin lines (the grid).

Look for the **5** along the right side of the map and go left between the lines.

Where **H** and **5** meet you find UNITED STATES (If you have written the name in the correct place).

On map indexes, the letter I is sometimes taken out because it is easy to mix up with the number 1 and the letter J.

Answers to questions on pages 36 and 37:

Page 6
1 Longitudes and Latitudes together are called the graticule or grid
2 The Equator

Page 7
1 Because each person's hand is individual, your answer will vary But your answer should be exactly half of the original measurement
2 It is 2 inches

Page 8-9
1 1:500,000
2 200+ miles up

Page 10-11
1 South-West
2 To the south

Page 12
1 Ottawa.
2 22 countries including the Caribbean.
3 It's the big island, Greenland.
4 The Pacific Ocean

Page 13
1 In the middle of the Panama Canal.
2 Antigua and Barbuda, and Uruguay.
3 In Antarctica.

Pages 14-15
1 Estonia, Latvia, Lithuania, Belarus, Moldova, Ukraine, Russia.

2 To the north: Norway
To the south: Malta
3 Atlantic Ocean

Pages 16-17
1 Africa has 52 countries
2 To the north: Europe
To the east: Asia
3 It is in the Red Sea and the Suez Canal.

Pages 18-19
1 Yes it is
2 Japan
3. Nepal

Page 20
1 Australia, New Zealand, Fiji and Tuvalu.

Page 21
1 North America, Europe and Asia
2 The Atlantic Ocean and the Arctic Ocean
3 South America, Africa and Asia
4. The South Pole

Pages 22-23
1 South America is the continent Latin America ithe region where people speak Spanish or Portuguese
2 There are 5 rings
3 Iceland, Denmark, Norway, Sweden, Finland.

Page 24-25
1 Leif Eriksson, and several hundred years later, Christopher Columbus

2 Magellan
3 Australia

Pages 26-27
1 Pluto
2 Saturn and Uranus
3 Our Earth
4 Saturn

Pages 28-29
1 It is night time
2 It is 6 o'clock p.m.
3 Eight time zones. Part of Canada
4 Cuba, Nicaragua, Colombia, Canada, Peru.

Pages 30-31
1 It is winter
2 The countries along the equator

Pages 32-33
1 In the geological middle ages.
2 Approximately 70 million years old.
3 Approximately 70 million years old.

Notes

Page 3 COLORING KEY
Fold out this page, which is the Coloring Key, so you can look at it for guidance when you color your MapBook. Look for the small letters in the flags and maps which match the letters and colors in the key. When you don't find coloring letters, you can use whatever colors you like.

Page 4 COLORING TIPS
You will learn a lot about different coloring ideas if you read this page. If you don't have all the colors- don't worry, you can mix the colors you have and get good results anyhow.

Page 5 TITLE PAGE
On the first page in any book, a lot of funny stuff is written. You can read on the title page of your book what it means. An explanation of 'copyright': For example, if you have made a very good drawing, maybe the best you have ever done, and someone copies that drawing without asking you if they have the right to do so. Maybe they even won first prize with their drawing, and then you feel bad about it. They should have asked you for the right to copy your work. This is copyright or © for short.

Page 6 MAP MAKER
A map would be easier to make if the Earth were flat. However, since the time the Greek Aristotle discovered that the Earth was round, the only way to picture it correctly is to make a small round model, a globe. The flat map you can make from the round balloon will help you to better understand how maps are laid out. Most maps, like your balloon map, are more accurate at the central equator and more inaccurate at the upper North Pole area and the lower South Pole area.
Questions:
1 What are the lines on the map called?
2 What is the horizontal line round the middle of the earth called?

Page 7 SCALE
When you want to draw a picture of the Earth or a part of it on a piece of paper, you have to show the Earth much smaller than it is in real life. You draw it in a smaller scale. Your Coloring Book, here in its actual size, is 1:1 (one inch in real life is one inch if you draw a picture of it).
Make a drawing of your MapBook in scale 1:2 (one inch on your drawing equals 2 inches in real life).
Then draw the Book in scale 1:10 (ten times smaller than it really is). Then try 1:100 (tricky!).
Cut out the ruler on page 39 and use it to measure scales.
Questions:
1 Measure your hand with a ruler. Now calculate how big your hand would be on the 1:2 scale?
2 How long is 8 inches at scale 1:4?

Pages 8 and 9 FROM A PICTURE TO A MAP
Color the pictures and also the maps on this page. Look at the map of the sandbox in the lower left corner. Try to find the same area on the map of the house in the middle drawing and draw a red square around it. Now try to find the house area on the neighborhood map to the right and draw a red square around it. Do the same with the other pictures.
Questions:
1 In what scale will you see the ground if you are 36,000 feet/9,000 meters up?
2 How high up do you have to fly to see a whole continent?

Page 10 DIRECTIONS
Directions like 'North' and 'South' are an international language. The red needle on a compass always points north, whether you are in Los Angeles or London. If you point east, the direction is the same wherever you are on Earth. The reason the compass needle points north is because there is a huge magnetic field close to the North Pole.
Questions:
1 What direction is between South and West?
2 If you stand with your nose to the sun at 12 o'clock noon in Chicago, in which direction does your back face?

Page 11 CAPTAIN COOK'S TREASURE MAP
Color the treasure in the colors of your choice. There are more routes to take you safely to the treasure than Captain Cook describes. Let your friends try, too!

Pages 12 and 13 NORTH AMERICA and
SOUTH AMERICA
Flags are important national symbols. The bright colors and bold patterns on a flag stand for the country's land, its people, its government, and its ideals. The first flag was used by the Italian city Genoa in the year 1198. You have also seen the international flags of the United Nations and the Red Cross (pages 22-23). Color the flags with the colors shown by the "color letter". Color all the countries with the color coding from the Color Key or with colors you choose yourself.
Look for the number under each flag and find the same number on the map. Write the country name on the dotted line. Look for the black dot under each flag. The name by the dot is the capital of that country. Find the capital-dot in each country, and write the name by the side of the dot. On each map there is a scale-bar at the bottom of the page. You can use it to measure distances on the map. The small airplane tells you how far a modern passenger aircraft can fly in one hour.
Questions: Page 12
1 Which city is the capital of Canada?
2 How many countries are there in North America? (Hint: also look on page 13.)
3 One part of North America belongs to a country in Europe. Which?
4 Which country has one part in North America and one part in South America?
5 In which ocean do you find Hawaii?

Questions: Page 13
1 Where does South America end and North America begin?
2 Which countries have a sun on their flag?
3 Where do you end up if you go south from the southern tip of Chile?

Pages 14 and 15 EUROPE
Questions:
1 The Soviet Union has split up into new countries. Some of them are in Europe. What are the names of these new countries? There are seven in Europe.
2 Which country in Europe is the furthest north?
3 Which country in Europe is the furthest south?
4 Which ocean lies between Europe and North America?